SPIKE'S SPECS

Elizabeth Dale

Illustrated by

ANTHONY LEWIS

HEINEMANN · LONDON

For my parents, with much love.

First published in 1994
by William Heinemann Ltd
an imprint of Reed Consumer Books Ltd
Michelin House
81 Fulham Road
London SW3 6RB

LONDON · MELBOURNE · AUCKLAND

Text © Elizabeth Dale 1994
Illustrations © Anthony Lewis 1994
ISBN 0 434 97809 4

Printed in Great Britain by William Clowes Ltd

A school pack of BANANA BOOKS 61-66 is
available from Heinemann Educational Books
ISBN 0 435 00096 9

1

NOTHING WOULD HAVE happened if Spike had been good; if he hadn't put Bartholomew, his pet spider, inside Mr Andrews' track-suit trousers (just to keep him warm) while he played football.

Everyone thought it was hilarious when Mr Andrews discovered Bartholomew crawling up his leg. Everyone except Mr Andrews.

'Samuel Ickroyd!' he bellowed.

'You're banned from the team for the next six weeks.'

Spike was the best goal-scorer the team had ever had, and his friends all groaned and pleaded with Mr Andrews to change his mind. But he just shook his head. When the names of the team for Saturday's match were pinned up, Spike's was not there.

'You'll just have to come to the
Brownie jumble sale with me, instead,'
said his mum, when he told her.

'Oh no!' protested Spike. 'It'll be all
smelly and full of stupid, giggly girls!'

'It won't be that bad!' said his mum.
'Tell you what, I'll give you 20p to
spend.'

Only 20p! Spike couldn't believe his
ears!

'50p,' he said.

'20p,' said his mother. 'And *only* if
you're very good.'

2

THE JUMBLE SALE *was* full of giggly girls, running around and trying to look important. But at least it wasn't smelly.

With his measly 20p in his hand, Spike ran off to investigate the toy table. But it was full of dolls and girls' things, so Spike went off to see what else there was.

And then, beneath a pile of socks, he saw it. He couldn't believe it! A denim jacket. Lovingly, he fingered it. All his life he'd wanted a denim jacket, but his mum wouldn't let him have one because she said they looked tatty, even when new. Didn't she realise, that was the point! This one even had tears in it.

'50p,' said the Brownie behind the counter.

'What?' gasped Spike. 'The other clothes are 10p.'

'This is a highly fashionable jacket!' she said.

'But it's torn!'

'Thank you for pointing that out!' she said. 'It costs extra for that, 60p!'

Spike glared at her. 'No way!' he said.

'I'll buy it then!' she said, grabbing it.

'I saw it first!' said Spike,

snatching it back. 'I'll just have to ask my mum.'

Of course, he wasn't going to give his mum a chance to say 'No.'

Instead, he showed it to an old lady behind another counter.

'Jackets are 40p,' she said.

'But it's all faded and torn!' said Spike, showing her.

The lady tut-tutted. 'In that case,

lovey, you can have it for 10p,' she said.

Spike was so pleased, he bought his mother a blouse with the change. It looked rather big, but it hid the denim jacket in his bag, so his mum couldn't see it and tell him to take it back. That was the main thing!

'What've you got there?' his mum asked, suspiciously.

'A present for you,' smiled Spike.

His mum stared at him, open-mouthed. He'd bought something for her! Obviously not playing football on a Saturday had affected his brain!

'I bought something for me for 10p as well,' said Spike. 'I hope you don't mind?'

'Of course not, darling,' said his mum, tearfully.

3

THAT EVENING, SPIKE was parading up
and down in his jacket in front of his
mum's long-length mirror, when he
discovered a pair of red specs in the
pocket.

At first, he was going to throw them
out. But then, for fun, he tried them
on, and amazingly, they looked really
cool, especially with his jacket. He ran
straight round to Daniel's. George was
there, too, talking about the match!

Suddenly, Spike realised he hadn't given it a moment's thought since he got his jacket.

'What a jacket!' exclaimed George. 'And as for those specs, why, you look like something off the planet Egghead!'

George rolled about the bed laughing, but Spike didn't notice. Something very strange was happening. A reddish tinge was spreading all over his lenses.

'Be fair!' said Daniel. 'That jacket's really cool!'

'It would be, with all those tears in it!' laughed George. But Spike wasn't listening. For as soon as Daniel started to speak, the reddish tinge disappeared. He blinked. Perhaps he'd imagined the whole thing?

'Hey, we haven't told you about

Paul Davies!' exclaimed George. 'He
was utterly brilliant in your place! I
reckon you're out of the team for
good!'

Spike stared at him, horrified. Out of
the team! He was so devastated, that he
hardly noticed that the redness had
come back in front of his eyes. 'He
didn't... he didn't score a goal, did he?'
he asked.

'A goal?' exclaimed George. 'No, he didn't score a goal, he scored ten! He was totally wicked!'

Desperately, Spike turned to Daniel. At the sight of his face, Daniel burst into laughter.

'He's winding you up!' he gasped. 'Paul was useless!'

It was only when the red tinge disappeared that Spike realised it had been there at all. He took off his specs, gave them a clean, and George a thump.

'Can I try them on?' asked Daniel. Spike passed them to him. 'What do I look like?' he asked, putting them on.

'Superman when he isn't being Superman,' said Spike.

'Elton John on an off-day,' said George.

Daniel took the glasses off, frowning.

'They're not much good,' he said. 'Who wants red-tinted glasses?'

'I think they react to the heat or something,' said Spike. 'They keep changing.'

'Let me try!' said George, putting them on. He looked silly.

'You look daft,' said Spike. 'Are they still red?'

George shook his head.

13

'Anyway, about the match,' said Daniel. 'Paul let three goals in! Mr Andrews was mad!'

'Really?' smiled Spike.

'Yes!' said Daniel. 'His face went red, his ears purple, he jumped up and down like a demented hedgehog!'

'Hey, these glasses have gone red!' exclaimed George.

'Do be quiet!' said Spike, taking the specs off him and putting them back on.

'Did he say anything about me?' he asked Daniel. 'How he'd have me back in the team next week?'

Daniel shook his head. 'I'm sure he will, though,' he said.

The specs went red.

'You told me you thought Mr Andrews would never have Spike back!' said George. 'Even if we lost twenty-nil.'

The specs cleared again.

Spike should have been upset, but he wasn't. For suddenly the most amazing idea had occurred to him.

'Tell me a lie!' he told Daniel. 'The biggest whopper you can think of!'

'What?' asked Daniel.

'Mr Andrews is my favourite person of all time!' said George.

The specs went red! Spike got really excited.

'Now tell me something true!'

'I hate school dinners!' said Daniel. The redness went away.

'Another lie!' ordered Spike.

'Um... my mum thinks I'm an angel!' said George. Everything was red again.

'What's all this about?' asked Daniel.

'Just a minute!' said Spike. 'First of all, tell me something... something I don't know, and I'll tell you if it's true!'

'Er... Mr Andrews goes to bed in a nightshirt!'

'True!' exclaimed Spike, as the glasses stayed clear. 'Am I right?'

'Haven't the faintest!' said George.

Spike glared at him. 'I meant tell me something you know but I don't!'

'I had sausages for breakfast!' said Daniel.

'False!' said Spike, as the specs went red.

'Yes I did!' said Daniel. But the glasses stayed red.

'Are you sure?' Spike asked. 'Really, really sure?'

'Yes,' said Daniel. 'I had six. I should know!'

'Oh,' said Spike, dejectedly. He'd almost believed...

'Wait!' yelled Daniel. 'That was yesterday! Today I didn't have any breakfast. I got up too late!'

'Brilliant!' exclaimed Spike, leaping up and down on the bed. 'I knew it! I just knew it! These specs are magic! They go red when people are telling lies!'

'Rubbish!' said George.

'Try them yourself,' said Spike.

They did, asking each other all kinds of ridiculous questions, and each time the specs got them right.

'They're amazing!' said George. 'I want a pair. Where did you get them?'

Spike told them. Both George and Daniel looked at him enviously.

'We can all have fun with them,' said Spike. 'I can't wait to take them to school. We can discover all the teachers' secrets.'

4

LATER THAT EVENING, Spike settled down to read while his father was watching the news. Suddenly, Spike's glasses turned red. He looked up, surprised. A government minister was being interviewed about the economy.

'I see a far brighter future in the next few months!' he said.

'No he doesn't,' said Spike.

'Of course he doesn't!' muttered his father. 'These politicians never tell the truth!'

'I have no plans to increase taxes,' he said.

'He has!' exclaimed Spike. 'He has!'

'What?' asked his father. 'How come you're suddenly such an expert?'

'Um, can't you tell by his eyes?' said Spike.

Next, an explorer on the screen said he wasn't scared about undertaking his lone expedition to the North Pole (which he was).

Then the weather forecaster said it was going to rain the next day (it wasn't). Suddenly, thanks to his glasses, everything, even the news, was interesting.

Spike sat up even more as the local news came on. There had been a robbery at a local jewellers' shop, and the only eyewitness was explaining how he saw a dark-haired man drive off with the jewels in a red car.

'He didn't!' exclaimed Spike as his specs turned red.

'What?' said his dad. 'Were you there? Did you see it all?'

'No, er, look, maybe I imagined it,' said Spike, excitedly. 'I'm just popping round to Daniel's.'

5

DANIEL HAD SEEN about the robbery on
TV, too.

'Just think of it, all those diamonds
stolen!' he exclaimed. 'In our High
Street.'

'I'm sure that man on the TV's the
robber!' said Spike, excitedly.

'What?'

'My specs went red. He was lying.
And why else would he lie but to give
the police a false trail?'

'Wow! What shall we do?' asked
Daniel.

'Get George,' said Spike.

George thought they ought to tell the police about the magic powers of the glasses.

'Well I'm not telling them!' exclaimed Spike. 'They'd roll about with laughter.'

'So we just sit back and let the robber get away with it?' asked George.

'No,' said Spike. 'We find him ourselves!'

'That's impossible!' said George.

'No it isn't,' said Daniel. 'There must be a way.'

'I know,' said Spike. 'My specs will tell us where he lives. We just need a local map, listing all the streets, and we can go through them until the specs say we've got the right one.'

'But why bother to do that?' asked George. 'We know where he lives.'

'What!' gasped Daniel and Spike.

'It was in the evening paper, and his name. I'll get it!'

George rushed home and returned with the paper.

'It's even got a photograph,' said
Spike. 'Brilliant! Mr Stephen Perkins of
Acacia Avenue, that's our man!'

'Right, specs on, let's work our way
through the numbers,' said Daniel. 'Mr
Stephen Perkins lives at the following
address, 1, Acacia Avenue...'

Spike shook his head.

'2, Acacia Avenue, 3, Acacia Avenue...'

By the time he got to 279, Acacia Avenue they started to think something might be wrong.

'How long's a normal avenue?' asked Daniel, hoarsely.

'Maybe your specs have gone wrong?' asked George.

Spike shook his head.

'Wait!' said Daniel. 'Stephen Perkins lives in Acacia Avenue...'

'No he doesn't!' said Spike. 'The specs have gone red!'

'But..?'

'He gave a false address,' said George. 'He *must* be the robber. Maybe he gave a false name, too?'

'He did,' said Spike, as the specs stayed clear. 'That's fantastic.'

He and Daniel leapt up and down,
but George sat still and looked glum.

'Don't you realise?' he said, slowly.
'It means we know nothing about this
man!'

'I'd better get the street map,' said
Daniel, wearily.

They read out the names of all the
streets and each time the specs stayed

red, until they got to Dawson Drive.

'That's it!' said Spike. 'Now which number? 1 ... 2 ... 3 ...'

On 25 the specs changed from red to clear. 'Brilliant!' said Daniel.

Just then Daniel's mum announced they had to go home.

'Never mind,' said Spike. 'We're almost there. No school tomorrow. We're going round to 25, Dawson Drive to catch us a jewel-thief!'

6

WITH THE HELP of Daniel's map, it was
easy to find the right house the next
morning. Or was it? 25, Dawson Drive
was a smart detached house with a
gravel drive and neat flower borders,
not at all like a robber's.

'I wonder if we've got it all wrong?'
asked George.

'There's one way to find out,' said
Spike. 'Hide behind the hedge until I
return.' And before they could stop

him, he strode noisily up the drive.

The others hid behind the hedge and waited. And waited.

'I don't like it,' said George, 'everything's too quiet...'

'I'm going in after him!' said Daniel.

'No!' yelled George.

'What's all the shouting about?' asked Spike, turning the corner.

'You're safe!' cried George.

'Where were you?' asked Daniel.

'There was no answer to the doorbell, so I went round the back, to make sure no one was in. Guess what I found?'

'The diamonds?' asked George, breathlessly.

'No, dumbo! They're hardly likely to leave the diamonds out by the dustbins, are they? But I did find a window open.'

George and Daniel stared at him.

'You're not going to do what I think you're going to do, are you?' asked George.

'Of course I am,' said Spike. 'If we can find the diamonds, and take one to the police, they'll have to believe us!'

'I don't like it...' said George.

'It's all right, George,' said Spike.

'You can be our look-out. You know what the thief looks like. If you see him coming down the road, run up the drive and ring the doorbell three times! We'll run out the back way!'

'All right,' said George reluctantly. 'But I don't like it!'

It was far more difficult to find the diamonds than Spike and Daniel had thought. The house was large and there were so many rooms! Finally, Spike hit on the idea of using his specs. Each time they got to a room, Daniel would say, 'The diamonds are in here,' and each time the specs went red. Until the last room, when they stayed clear.

'This is it!' yelled Spike, and together they charged into the room, so intent on looking under the bed, that they didn't notice there was someone still asleep in it...

Suddenly a loud scream came from
the house. Outside, George froze. It
was Spike, he was sure of it! He peered
round the hedge. Through a front
bedroom window, a man could be
clearly seen. Was it the robber? What
should he do? And then George did the
one thing his instincts had been telling
him to do all along. He ran.

'So, which of you two is going to tell me what's going on?' demanded the robber.

Spike looked out of the corner of his eye at Daniel. They were both lying on the bed, face down, and the robber had a mean expression on his face and a gun in his hand.

'We were just messing around,' said Spike. 'We thought the house was empty.'

'Oh, yes?' said the man. 'Come on, I wasn't born yesterday! You came here because you knew something, didn't you? Who else have you told?'

'Told what?' asked Daniel, innocently.

'I'm not playing games!' said the robber, throwing some rope at Spike. 'You! Tie your friend's hands together, real tight. If there's any loose knots, I'm going to be very angry!'

Spike looked at the gun. It was black and menacing.

'I suppose that thing's loaded?' he asked.

The robber laughed. "Course it is,' he said.

Suddenly, the ringing of the doorbell made them all jump. Spike looked out of the window. A police car was parked outside!

'One sound out of you, and you're dead!' hissed the robber, pointing his gun menacingly at the boys.

The bell rang again. It echoed through the empty house. And then there was the crunch of footsteps on gravel. They were going away! But they mustn't!

'Help! We're up here!' Spike yelled at the top of his voice.

The robber launched himself at the door, but somehow Spike's foot was in the way, and he went sprawling.

He was just picking himself up when
the police burst in. Within seconds,
they'd handcuffed him.

When all danger was past, George
walked in.

'Thanks, George, you were brilliant
to get the police so quickly,' said Spike.

George smiled. He'd never been a hero before.

'You were brave, Spike, shouting out like that,' said Daniel. Spike opened his mouth to say that his specs had told him that the gun wasn't loaded, but he closed it again. After all, the robber was big and mean, so it was still brave to tackle him, wasn't it?

The Inspector looked in the robber's sack and pulled out a brooch that sparkled so much it was positively dazzling. Everyone gasped.

'What's that?' demanded the robber. 'Those kids put it here! It's a plant!'

'Oh yes? And that gun is a rose bush, is it?' laughed the policeman. He turned to Spike. 'How on earth did you know the jewels were here?'

Daniel and George looked at Spike.

'I just knew,' said Spike. 'When I saw

him on the TV talking about the
robbery, I just knew he was lying. So
we tracked him down.'

'What amazing powers you have!' said the Inspector. 'You certainly deserve the reward.'

The boys looked at each other, amazed.

'What reward?' asked Daniel.

'£500,' said the Inspector. 'Don't tell me you didn't know anything about it!'

But Spike, George and Daniel couldn't tell him anything. They were speechless!

Of them all, Spike was the happiest. Not only had he caught a robber and earned a reward, he'd still got his specs. He could have weeks, years of fun with them, at school, at home, everywhere. And maybe he'd solve even more crimes!